BY THE EDITORS OF CONSUMER GUIDE®

PIANO PLAYING
POPULAR SONGS
Made Easy

For the Advanced Beginner

PUBLICATIONS INTERNATIONAL, LTD.

Introduction

Piano Playing: Popular Songs Made Easy will teach you to play all-time favorite songs and will provide the practice you need to improve your playing. If you have just a little experience playing the piano and wish to continue this satisfying hobby, or if you are unsure about spending the time and money for lessons, then this do-it-yourself book is for you.

As you progress through *Piano Playing: Popular Songs Made Easy*, you will be introduced to skills in a systematic and logical way. This book is organized around 12 lessons. Each lesson concentrates on a specific skill and includes short exercises to practice and pieces to play using that skill. By the time you are finished you will be playing popular standards like "Danny Boy," "The Entertainer," and "Stars and Stripes Forever" for your own enjoyment and for the enjoyment of your family and friends. Remember, improving your piano playing takes patience, discipline, and practice. Don't get discouraged and, most importantly, don't forget to have fun!

Copyright © 1995 Publications International, Ltd. All rights reserved. This book may not be reproduced or quoted in whole or in part by mimeograph or any other printed or electronic means, or for presentation on radio, television, videotape, or film without written permission from:

Louis Weber, C.E.O.
Publications International, Ltd.
7373 North Cicero Avenue
Lincolnwood, Illinois 60646

Permission is never granted for commercial purposes.

Manufactured in USA.

8 7 6 5 4 3 2 1

ISBN 0-7853-2097-0

Contributing Writer: Gilbert DeBenedetti

Gilbert DeBenedetti teaches music theory at the Pittsburgh High School for the Creative and Performing Arts and the University of Pittsburgh at Greensburg. He holds a Master of Arts in music theory and composition from the University of Pittsburgh. He is the author of *The Creative Pianist,* four books for beginning piano students that encourage composition.

Illustrations: Leonid Mysakov (cover), Kat Thacker.

Contents

Music Reading Review

The Grand Staff

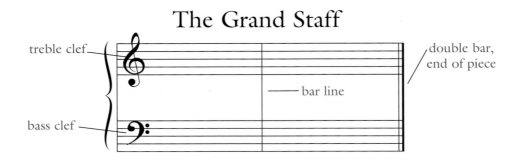

treble clef

bass clef

bar line

double bar, end of piece

The Grand Staff and the Keyboard

This book assumes some familiarity with these notes.

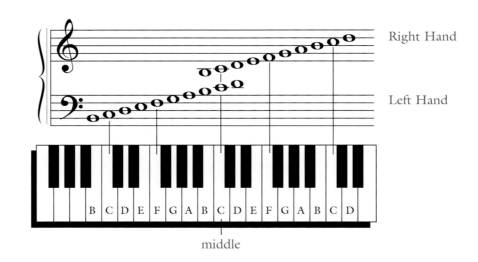

Right Hand

Left Hand

B C D E F G A B C D E F G A B C D

middle

Notes and Rests

Name	eighth	2 eighths	quarter	dotted quarter and eighth		half	dotted half	whole
Note	♪	♫	♩	♩.	♪	𝅗𝅥	𝅗𝅥.	𝅝
Rest	𝄾		𝄽			▬	▬.	▬
Count	and	1 and	1	1-2	and	1-2	1-2-3	1-2-3-4

the whole rest is also used for a whole measure

Sharps, Flats, and Naturals

F sharp

G flat

F natural

Cancels a sharp or flat. Sharps and flats normally apply to all subsequent notes with the same letter name. When an F natural is written, play F.

Time Signatures

four beats in each measure

the quarter note is one beat (or count) long

three beats in each measure

the quarter note is one beat (or count) long

Finger Numbers

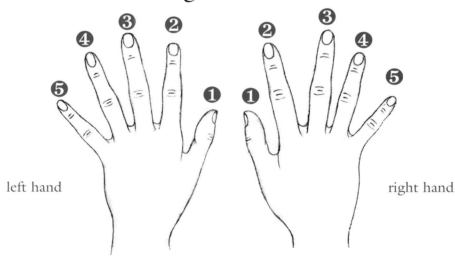

left hand   right hand

Terms

𝆑   short for forte, Italian for **loud**

𝆏   short for piano, Italian for **soft**

𝄐   a **fermata**. Hold the note for longer than its usual number of beats.

D.C. al Fine   short for **Da Capo al Fine**. Go back to the beginning and play until the word "Fine."

Fine   Italian for **end**

rit.   short for ritardando. Play **gradually slower** and slower.

           A curved line between two notes of the same pitch is a **tie**. Do not play the note again. Instead, hold the note for the duration of both notes.

LESSON 1
C AND F POSITIONS

In Lesson 1 the low note of each hand is usually C or F, and the high note is usually five notes above. There are occasional stretches up or down one note.

Chords in C and F Positions

THIS OLD MAN

This old man, He played one, He played nick nack on my thumb with a

nick nack pat-ty wack give the dog a bone, This old man came roll-ing home.

ANGELS WE HAVE HEARD ON HIGH

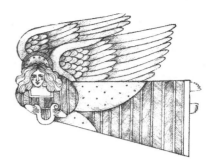

An - gels we have heard on high, Sweet - ly sing - ing o'er the plains,
And the mountains in re - ply Ech - o - ing their joy - ous strains,

Glo ri - a

in ex - cel - sis De - o, Glo

ri–a in ex - cel - sis De o.

Moving From C to F Position

Practice this exercise hands separately, then hands together.

HOME ON THE RANGE

Oh, give me a home where the buf-fa-lo roam, Where the

deer and the an-te-lope play. Where sel-dom is heard a dis-

A GERMAN WALTZ: DU, DU, LIEGST MIR IM HERZEN

RISE AND SHINE

$\frac{6}{8}$ Time

The time signature $\frac{6}{8}$ means that each measure is six-eighth notes long. Count to six for each measure as you practice. Then try to feel two beats in each measure, each a dotted quarter note long. Also try to hear the quarter, eighth note rhythm as "slow quick." Practice this exercise hands separately, then hands together.

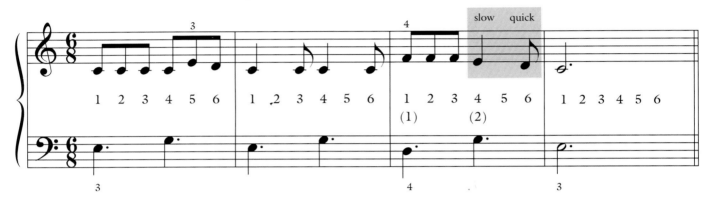

ROW, ROW, ROW YOUR BOAT

OVER THE RIVER

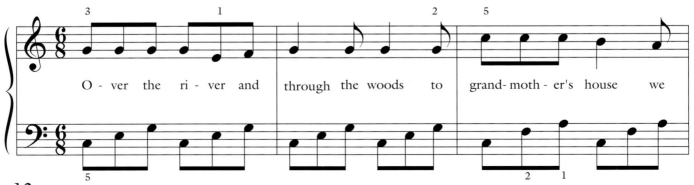

O - ver the ri - ver and through the woods to grand- moth - er's house we

go.——————— The horse knows the way to car-ry the sleigh through cold and drift-ing snow.——————— O-ver the ri-ver and through the woods, Oh how the wind does blow.——————— It stings the nose and bites the toes as o-ver the hills we go.

LESSON 3
G POSITIONS

The music in Lesson 3 is in *G position*.
Place your left hand so that your thumb
is on the D above middle C. Place your
right thumb on the note G.

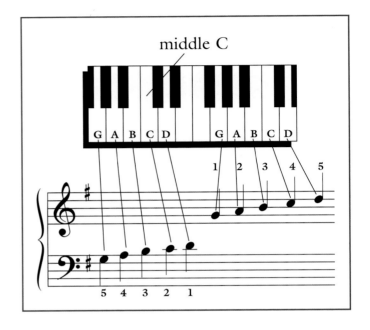

LIGHTLY ROW

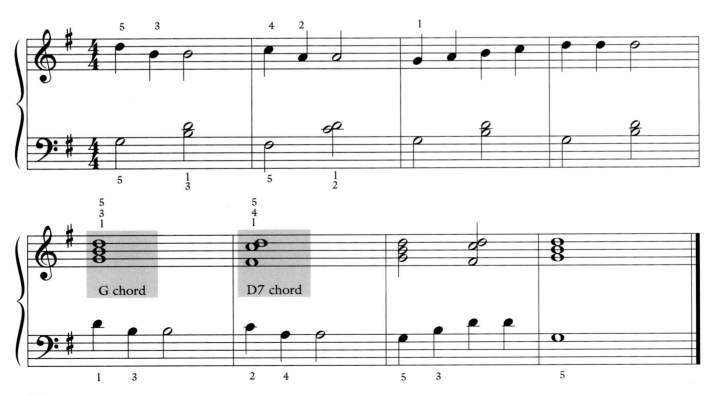

Practice Eighth Notes with a Swing

Popular musicians often add a "swing" to their eighth notes. They play the first eighth note of a pair slower than the second. Practice this swing in the following exercise.

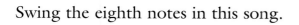

Swing the eighth notes in this song.

HE'S GOT THE WHOLE WORLD

The following exercise and piece demonstrates the *low G position*. Place your left hand so that it is an octave below standard G position.

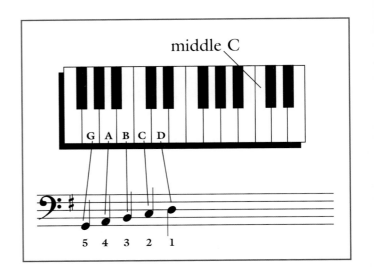

Practice in Low G Position

SHOO, FLY

Shoo, fly, Don't bo-ther me, Shoo, fly, don't bo-ther me,

LESSON 4
UP A FOURTH

Moving up a Fourth
to Standard G Position

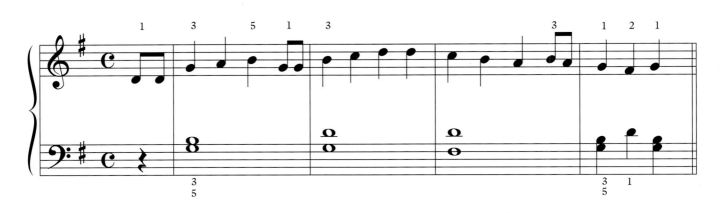

A-HUNTING WE WILL GO

f A - hunt - ing we will go, A - hunt - ing we will

Lyrics under the staff: go, We'll put a fox in - side a box, And then we'll let him go.

Notes of the Treble Clef

Learn to read notes of the treble clef independently of hand positions.
The letter for the spaces are F, A, C, and E, as in the word "FACE."
The letters for the lines are E, G, B, D, and F, as in the phrase, "Every Good Boy Does Fine."

F   A   C   E   Every   Good   Boy   Does   Fine

A small note with a slash is called a *grace note*. A grace note is
a quick note played just before the larger notes beside it.
Its duration is ignored when counting beats per measure.

REVEILLE

grace note

Fine

D. C. al Fine

D.S. al Fine at the end of the last line is short for *Dal Segno al Fine.* It means go back to the sign in the middle of line 2 and finish the piece at the word "Fine."

The **C** at the beginning of the first line is short for *common time,* another name for the time signature ⁴₄.

AULD LANG SYNE

Two-Note Slurs

A curved line between two notes which are not of the same pitch is called a *slur*. Slurred notes are played smooth and connected.

Usually the first note is louder and longer than the second note. To achieve this effect in the following exercise, bring your wrist down slightly when playing the first note of the pair, and bring your wrist up as you play the second note.

Practice this exercise slowly.

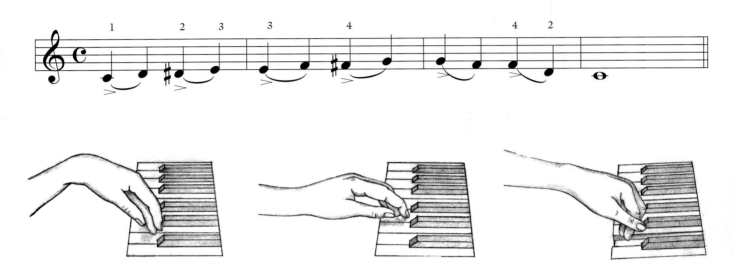

Step 1: Begin with wrist relaxed and raised.

Step 2: Keeping it relaxed, bring wrist down to play first note.

Step 3: Raise wrist as last note of phrase is played. Wrist should still be relaxed.

THE ARKANSAS TRAVELER

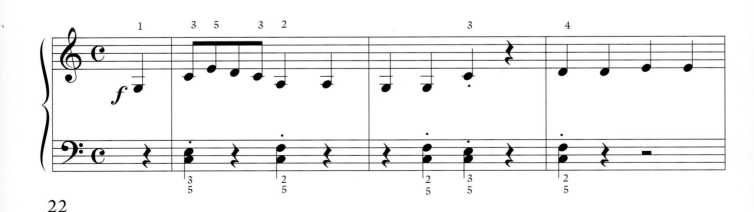

LESSON 5
STRETCH TO THE OCTAVE

In all the pieces in Lesson 5, there will be an octave stretch. In this exercise, keep your thumb and fifth finger close to the two Cs as you play the first two measures.

ON TOP OF OLD SMOKY

On top of old Smok - y,   All cov - ered with snow,   I lost my true lov - er   a - court - ing too slow.

24

Notes of the Bass Clef

Learn to read notes of the bass clef independently of hand positions.
The letters for the spaces are A, C, E, and G, as in the phrase "All Cows Eat Grass."
The letters for the lines are G, B, D, F, and A, as in the phrase "Good Boys Do Fine
Always."

All   Cows   Eat   Grass   Good   Boys   Do   Fine   Always

SWEET BETSY FROM PIKE

D'you ever hear tell of sweet Betsy from Pike Who
crossed the wide prairies with her husband Mike, With two yoke of cattle and
one spotted hog, A tall Shanghai rooster and old yellow dog.

The wedge-shaped symbol above the Bs in the first line is an *accent*.
Play these notes louder than the rest of the piece.

THE CAMPTOWN RACES

Stephen Foster

Camp-town la - dies sing this song, Doo- dah! Doo - dah! The

Camp- town race track's five miles long, Oh! doo-dah - day!

Going to ride all night, Going to ride all day, I'll—

bet my mo-ney on the bob- tail nag, Some - bo-dy bet on the bay.

LESSON 6
STRETCH TO A SEVENTH

All the pieces in Lesson 6 have a stretch to a seventh, one note less than an octave, in the left hand. Here is an exercise with this stretch for you to practice.

SWING LOW, SWEET CHARIOT

Swing low, sweet char - i ot   Com - ing for to · car - ry me home, Swing

low,   sweet   char - i ot,   Com - ing for to   car - ry me   home.

Prepare for the next two pieces with this exercise:

AMAZING GRACE

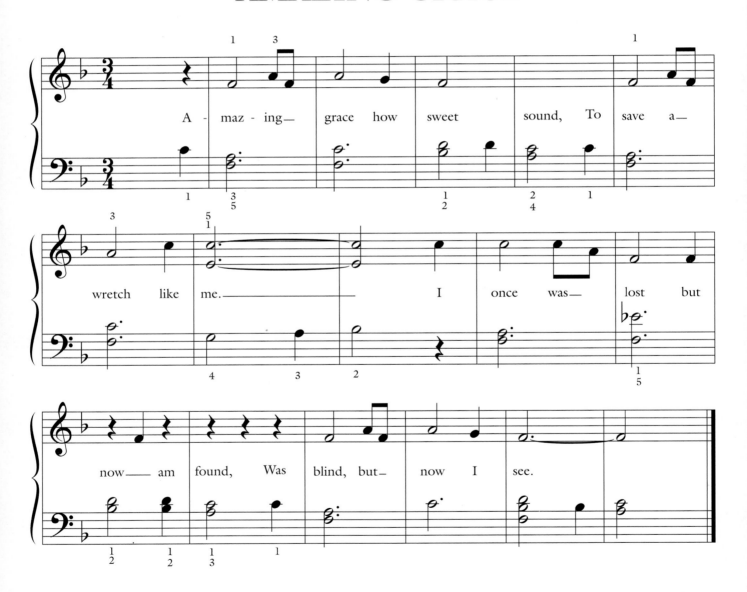

A - maz - ing— grace how sweet sound, To save a—

wretch like me._____ I once was— lost but

now— am found, Was blind, but— now I see.

28

RED RIVER VALLEY

1. From this Valley they say you are leav - ing, We will
2. Come and sit by my side if you love me, Do not

miss your bright eyes and sweet smile. For they
has - ten to bid me a - dieu, But re -

say you are tak - ing the sun - shine That___
mem - ber the Red Riv - er Val - ley, and the

bright - ens our path - way a - while._____
ones who have loved you so true.

LESSON 7
PLAYING HIGH NOTES

You will play these notes in the pieces in Lesson 7:

POLLY WOLLY DOODLE

SHE'LL BE COMING ROUND THE MOUNTAIN

Dots above or below notes indicate that those notes should be played *staccato,* short and detached. The 𝄵 with a slash through it at the beginning of the first staff means *cut time.* Music in cut time has two beats per measure, with each beat a half note long. Therefore, cut time can also be notated $\frac{2}{2}$.

DOWN BY THE RIVERSIDE

study war no more, I ain't gon-na study war no more,

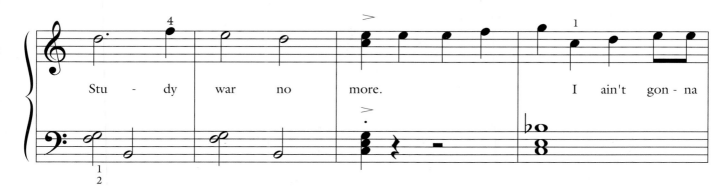

Stu - dy war no more. I ain't gon - na

study war no more, I ain't gon-na study war no more,

Stu - dy war no more.

Practice with Ledger Lines

High notes are sometimes notated with *ledger lines*. Ledger lines are short lines which go above, below, or through notes which are beyond the staff. Be familiar with the names of the notes with ledger lines in this exercise.

mf means "mezzo forte" or **medium loud.** *mp* means "mezzo piano" or **medium soft.**

AN AMERICAN MARCH: THE CAISSONS

LESSON 8
THE KEY OF D MINOR

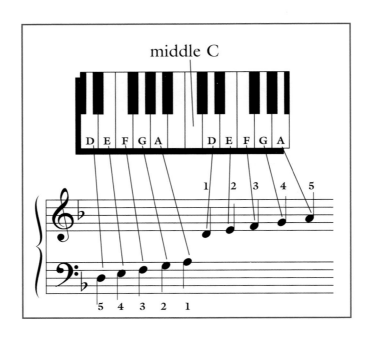

The music in Lesson 8 is in the key of D minor. You may notice that the key signature for D minor and F major are identical. Because of this, D minor is known as the *relative minor* of F major. First practice the exercise below with each hand separately. Then practice it with both hands together.

Practice in D Minor

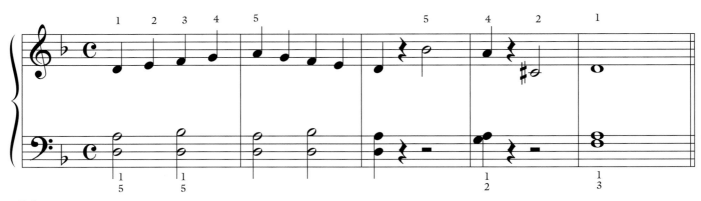

LET MY PEOPLE GO

p When Is - rael was in E - gypt's land, *f* Let my peo - ple go! *p* Op -

pressed so hard they could not stand, *f* Let my peo - ple go!

f Go down, Mo - ses, Way down in E - gypt's land——

Tell old Pha - roah to let my peo - ple go!

WHEN JOHNNY COMES MARCHING HOME

Louis Lambert

When Johnny comes marching home again, Hurrah! Hurrah! We'll give him a hearty welcome then, Hurrah! Hurrah! The men will cheer and the boys will shout, The ladies they will all turn out, and we'll all feel gay when Johnny comes marching home.

HEY, HO, NOBODY HOME

AURA LEE

D minor and A minor in the key of C

Civil War Song

LESSON 9
D AND A7 CHORDS

Practice in the Key of D

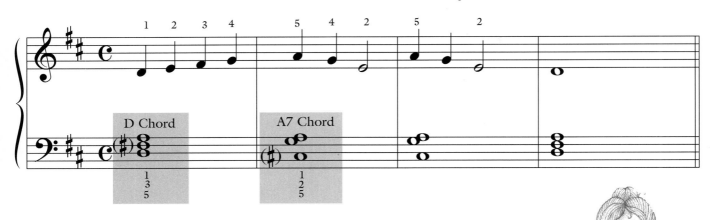

THE IRISH WASHERWOMAN

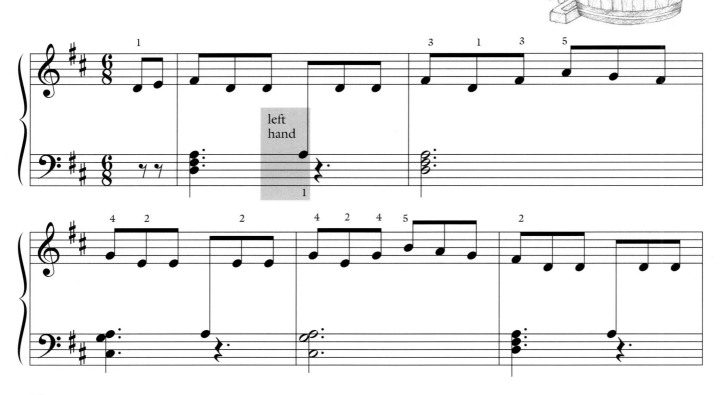

THE ENTERTAINER

Scott Joplin

Phrase Markers

Curved lines that span three or more notes are called *phrase markers*. The phrases marked by these lines are usually played with the notes connected smoothly to each other. There should be no silences between notes under a phrase marker. This kind of playing is called *legato*. In the following exercise and piece, contrast this legato sound with the staccato sound of the notes with dots over or under them.

TAKE ME OUT TO THE BALLGAME

Words: Jack Norworth
Music: Albert von Tilzer

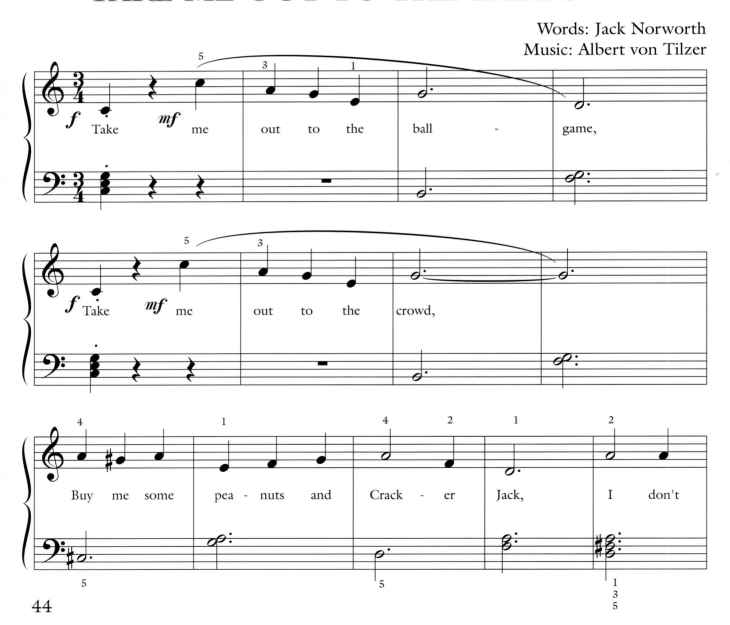

LESSON 10
THE DAMPER PEDAL

In the following pieces you will be using the *damper pedal*. The damper pedal is the pedal furthest to the right below the piano keyboard. Electric keyboards are sometimes sold with a damper pedal. This pedal prevents the sounds from being muted when a key is lifted. So the piano strings ring freely until the vibrations die down on their own.

When playing a piece in which this pedal is used, keep your right heel on the floor and the toes or ball of the right foot on the pedal at all times.

Press the pedal when a bracketed line appears under the music.

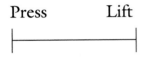

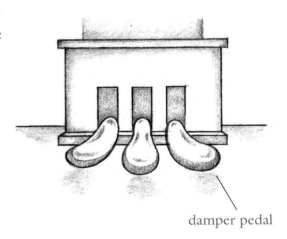

damper pedal

THE CHIMES

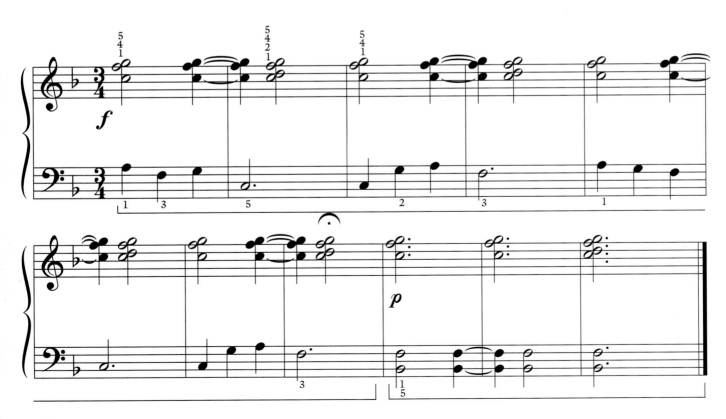

EVERY NIGHT WHEN THE SUN GOES IN

p Ev-'ry night when the sun goes in, Ev-'ry night when the sun goes in, Ev-'ry night when the sun goes in, I hang down my head and mourn-ful cry.

Overlapping Pedal Technique

A pointed break in the pedal line indicates *overlapping pedalling*. Overlapping pedalling creates a seamless flow to the music. To achieve this flow, lift the pedal at the same time that you play the notes above the pointed break. Then press down again after the notes are played. Do not lift before playing these notes or a silence will interrupt the flow.

Simile at the bottom of the page means play the music similarly until the end of the piece or until further instructions are given. In this case keep lifting the pedal every measure.

FLOW GENTLY SWEET AFTON

Words: Robert Burns
Music: Alexander Hume

48

The repeat sign in the last line means go back to the left repeat in the middle of line 2. Do not go back to the beginning.

The line above the measure with the repeat indicates that this is the *first ending*. After you have played the music a second time, skip and go to the *second ending*.

A RUSSIAN DANCE: KOROBUSHKA

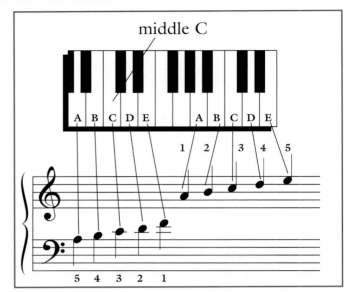

SCARBOROUGH FAIR

Are you going to Scar - borough fair?

Pars - ley, sage, rose - ma - ry and thyme, Re -

mem - ber me to one who lives there ____

She once was a true love of mine.

Practice with Descending Chords

In "A Spanish Dance: Fandango" and "Greensleeves" chords in the left hand descend one after another in order. Practice the first phrase of "God Rest Ye Merry Gentlemen" to get ready for these pieces.

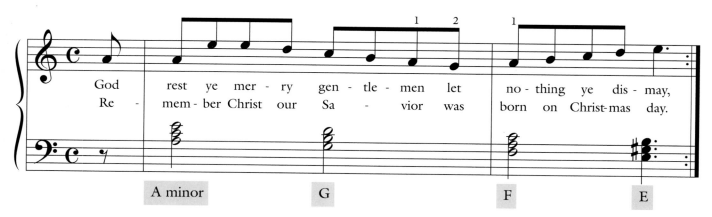

The following piece demonstrates a change in time signature. It begins and ends in common time, but remember to change to $\frac{3}{4}$ time for the middle.

A SPANISH DANCE: FANDANGO

Arpeggios in the Left Hand

In "Greensleeves" the left hand plays broken chords which span an octave. These broken chords are called *arpeggios*. Practice some arpeggios in this exercise:

GREENSLEEVES

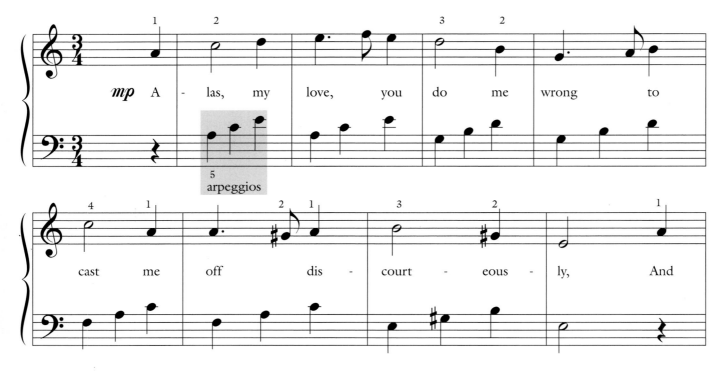

LESSON 12
LET'S PLAY PIANO

THE BLUE BELLS
OF SCOTLAND

Oh where, and oh where is your High - land lad - die

gone? He's gone to fight the foe for King

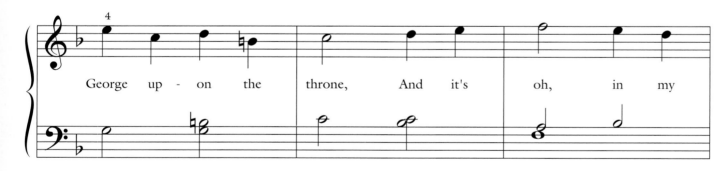

George up - on the throne, And it's oh, in my

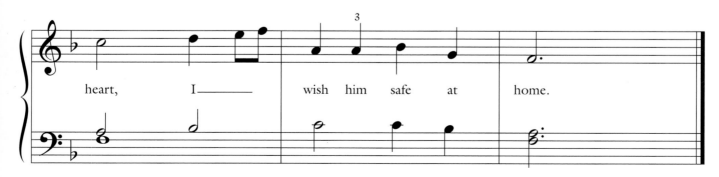

heart, I___ wish him safe at home.

THE YELLOW ROSE
OF TEXAS

There's a yel-low rose in Tex-as I'm go-ing back to see, She's

wait-ing there in Tex-as for me and on-ly me. She

cried so when I left her, 'Twas like to break her heart, And

when I'm home, no more to roam, We ne-ver more shall part.

DANNY BOY

Words: Fred E. Weatherly
Music: Traditional

O Dan - ny boy, the pipes, the pipes are call——ing, From glen to glen and down the mountain side, The summer's gone and all the flow-ers dy——ing, 'Tis you, 'tis you must

TARANTELLA

STARS AND STRIPES FOREVER

John Philip Sousa

SILENT NIGHT

Franz Gruber